Contents Contents Contents

Contents

Special Features

Features

The World of Plants

Written by Chantelle Greenhills

According to plant scientists, hundreds of millions of years ago the first land plants appeared on Earth. They looked nothing like the plants we see today. They have changed and developed over time as the conditions on Earth have changed, depending on their environment.

Today, there are thousands and thousands of different plants. They are truly amazing as they adapt themselves to survive in the difficult conditions of many places around the world, such as deserts, wetlands, and rain forests.

Plants of the Desert

Desert plants have to survive with minimal water. To enable them to do this, they have developed many features, for example, a lack of leaves but thick trunks; few pores that breathe during the cooler part of the day and night; long branching roots that either stay close to the ground or dig deep; an ability to come to life only during the wet seasons.

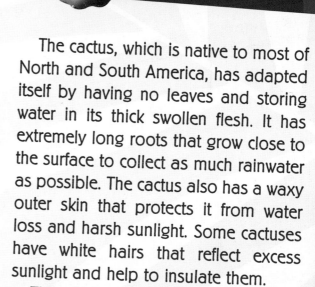

Prickly pear

Agave

The cactus, which is native to most of North and South America, has adapted itself by having no leaves and storing water in its thick swollen flesh. It has extremely long roots that grow close to the surface to collect as much rainwater as possible. The cactus also has a waxy outer skin that protects it from water loss and harsh sunlight. Some cactuses have white hairs that reflect excess sunlight and help to insulate them.

The cactus has a few small breathing holes. These are situated in the shady parts of the plant.

The agave plant is found in the southern US and tropical America. It has adapted itself by having thick juicy leaves that are filled with large cells that store water. These leaves are stiff and sharply pointed, and grow close to the ground. The outer leaves are covered with a waxy waterproofing. The leaves have a few pores that breathe at night.

Cactus

The creosote bush is found in Mexico and the western US. It has adapted itself by developing long, branching root systems that spread out just below the ground. This enables them to catch the slightest drop of rain.

Creosote bush

The desert mariposa lily of North America has adapted itself to desert life by coming to life only in spring after the winter rainfall. It grows from an underground bulb.

Desert mariposa lily

Tumboa

The tumboa is found in the deserts of Namibia. It has a single pair of huge flat leaves, although it can look as though there are many leaves because they are shredded into many parts by the wind. The plant has developed this way in order to soak up as much moisture as it can from the frequent fogs.

It can survive to a great age. Some tumboa plants are thought to be over 2,000 years old.

Plants of the Wetlands

The term *wetlands* refers to a wide variety of aquatic areas, for example, swamps, marshes, and bogs. Plants that grow in areas such as these, that are seasonally or permanently flooded, are known as hydrophytes. Hydrophytes need to be able to survive with a lot of water, and have adapted themselves to ensure that their roots get enough air.

The roots of the red mangrove arch into the air to get oxygen for the plant.

The red mangrove can be found in many Florida swamps where fresh and salt water meet. It is able to tolerate frequent deep flooding by having massive, stilt-like arching roots. These roots provide firm anchorage in the sloppy mud and a means of getting oxygen from the air. They also prevent much salt from entering the plant.

New mangroves are produced by seeds which, when fertilized, drop off or float away until they reach a mud bed where they send out side roots to immediately anchor themselves.

The black mangrove grows close to the red mangrove. It has adapted itself to cope with the salty water with leaves that are able to excrete excess salts, which drip down from the leaves.

Salt crystals on the leaves of a black mangrove

The waterlily grows in ponds and has adapted to the watery conditions in a number of ways. The waterlily's roots anchor the plant to the bottom of the pond. The waterlily is different from land-based plants, as it does not rely on its roots to take up water and nutrients. It can take in water and nutrients from any of its surfaces.

The leaves of the waterlily lie flat on the water and have adapted themselves by having breathing holes on the top of the leaf unlike most land-based plants, which have theirs on the bottom of the leaf. The floating leaves have a waxy surface to ensure that water runs off them easily. The stalks of the leaves have adapted themselves by being soft and bendable so that they don't break when water pushes against them.

It can take in water and nutrients from any of its surfaces.

Plants of the Rain Forest

Many plants of the rain forest have adapted to cope with excess moisture and very little sunlight. They grow in different layers within the forest and the plants at each layer have adapted in different ways.

Big trees emerge through the top of the rain forest.

Tall trees with smooth bark

The top layer of the rain forest is called the emergent layer and is made up of a few big trees that stand out above the rain-forest roof. One of the ways trees in this layer have adapted themselves to the excessive moisture and lack of sunlight is by having thin, smooth bark. This helps moisture to evaporate from the trees' trunks.

Another way they have adapted is by having large ridges near the base. These are called buttresses. It is thought that the buttresses may help to transport water and increase the area over which nutrients can be taken from the soil.

Buttresses

Some types of rain-forest plants grow on other plants or trees without harming them. These plants are called epiphytes.

The orchid is an epiphyte. It grows on the branches of the tallest trees so that it can get sunlight. The orchid has long, trailing aerial roots that take moisture from the air and store food and water.

Orchid growing on a tree

Bromeliads are plants that grow on the trunks or branches of other plants. They do this in order to get closer to the sunlight. They have adapted to the conditions of the rain forest by having thick waxy leaves, which form a bowl shape to catch rainwater.

Bromeliad

The next layer of the rain forest is called the canopy layer. It is made up of trees that grow together to form a roof that protects the lower trees from wind. However, these trees use up most of the sun's energy and block most of its light. Many of the trees at this layer look similar. Their leaves have adapted to cope with large amounts of rainfall by having a drip tip to enable rain to run off.

Trees in the canopy layer protect other trees and plants from wind but block sunlight.

Thick, woody vines can be found in the canopy layer. They are called lianas and have adapted to life in the rain forest by having their roots in the ground and climbing up and twining around trees to reach any available sunlight.

The next layer of the rain forest is called the understory. In this layer are vines, smaller trees, ferns, and palms. These plants receive very little sunlight or rainfall and have adapted themselves by not producing flowers, which helps conserve energy. They also have broad leaves, which allow them to take in any light that comes near and stay green all year round to help with food production.

Lianas twist and climb their way up to the sunlight.

Most of the plants that grow on the forest floor are fungi, mosses, or herbs.

The lowest layer of the rain forest is called the forest-floor layer. Little sunlight gets to the bottom of the rain forest. Most of the plants that grow on the forest floor are fungi, mosses, or herbs. They are known as saprophytes.

Saprophytes are plant organisms that break down dead, decaying animal and plant matter to add nutrients to the soil of the rain forest.

Safari POWER

Word Meanings

anchorage
a — heavy object
b — stable hold
c — spread

evaporate
a — emit moisture
b — absorb moisture
c — drip

evasive
a — elusive
b — friendly
c — quick

excess
a — bright
b — surplus
c — moderate

fragrance
a — plant name
b — bad smell
c — sweet smell

menacingly
a — threateningly
b — curiously
c — kindly

minimal
a — least possible
b — a lot
c — none at all

monotonous
a — quiet
b — exciting
c — unvarying

nutrients
a — toxins
b — bad soil
c — nourishment

pores
a — spikes
b — tiny openings
c — large holes

smother
a — cover and stifle
b — attack roughly
c — knock over

tolerate
a — bear
b — encourage
c — enjoy

Answers on page 21

10

A Country Garden

Written by Tracey Reeder

Clematis clings to an ancient arch.

Lavender leans across a pebbled path.

Frangipani fragrance floats in the aromatic air.

Sunflowers sway in the blustering breeze.

Rosemary reaches over the weather-beaten wall.

Willows weep down to the grassy ground.

Moss marches over jagged, ragged rocks.

Wisteria wanders over the mossy mound.

Daylilies delight, burnished bright in the summer sun.

And an old, old oak tree towers over them all,

The plants of my country garden – big and small.

Planet of the Plants

Written by
Rose Goldsmith

Illustrated by
Mike Moreu

"Something's got us, Captain," Franny Meizigger shouted, trying hard to keep her voice on an even keel. "Any idea what it might be?" asked Senna Santana.

"Let's have a closer look on the screen," Captain Carmela Carter suggested. "We should be able to identify any attacker that way."

"It looks like the roots of a gigantic plant," said Franny Meizigger, incredulously. "It has us wrapped up tighter than a birthday present."

"Computer, can you elaborate on this thing that has us trapped?" Captain Carter spoke into the minute microphone.

"It seems that Ms. Meizigger is correct," reported the computer in its robot-like monotone. "We have been trapped by the roots of a winter rye plant. The winter rye plant is known to have the longest roots of any plant. It is pulling us quickly in the direction of a small planet."

"Is the status of the planet friendly or unfriendly? asked Captain Carter.

"No report," replied Franny.

"Affirmative," reported the computer. "No status."

"Take evasive action," Captain Carter ordered.

"Too late, Captain," Franny responded. "Our systems are all down!"

Captain Carmela Carter and her crew, Senna Santana and Franny Meizigger, were on a mission into the fifth quadrant, charting little-visited planets as possible future settlement sites. But right now their ship was being pulled faster than a runaway roller coaster straight down in the direction of an unknown planet.

"Computer, transfer all power over to wrist controllers," barked Captain Carter into her microphone. "Franny and Senna, set stunners to five-minute freeze," she continued. "We don't know what we'll find on this planet, but the inhabitants have brought us here for a reason."

As she finished speaking, the winter rye plant settled them on the surface of the planet and gently unwound its long, sticky roots.

"Follow me," said Captain Carter, leading the way through the hatch.

The planet was lush and green. A gentle breeze wafted through some trees, and the sound of waves crashing in the distance indicated an ocean. There was no welcoming committee, but also no obvious threat of attack.

"Computer, scan the planet for life forms," ordered the captain.

"There seems to be an oversupply of oxygen on this planet," said the computer in its monotonous voice. "There is no sign of human life as we know it. However, my database shows that this planet is inhabited and run by plants. The ruler is a giant lindsay creek tree."

"Position of the giant lindsay creek tree?" asked Captain Carter.

"It's coastal," reported the computer. "The giant lindsay creek tree is a coastal redwood, situated almost directly on the shoreline."

Captain Carter and the others turned in the direction of the coast. They hadn't been walking for more than five minutes when Senna noticed a vile smell.

"Do you smell that?" she asked the others, holding her nose. "It's worse than week-old meat that's been rotting out in the sun."

"Status, computer?" asked Captain Carter.

"A flower," reported the computer, "called rafflesia arnoldi. Some people call it the stinking corpse lily."

"Stinking corpse is about it," Senna said, nauseated and trying hard not to gag. "Let's get out of here right now." And with that, she turned to go.

"Wait!" yelled Franny. "It could be a trap or decoy. Maybe we're supposed to skirt around the plant so that we get trapped by something else."

"Some people call it the stinking corpse lily."

"Computer?" Captain Carter said, her voice rising at the end of the word to signal a question.

"Scans show a large lichen-infested pit just to the left," responded the computer. "There is a hidden track going past the rafflesia arnoldi on the right. It seems Ms. Meizigger has made another correct assumption."

Trying not to retch, the three crew members made their way as quickly as possible past the stinking corpse lily, only to find the path blocked once again, this time by a thick grove of spiky cactus-type plants.

"Computer?" Captain Carter's voice rose again.

"This plant is called opuntia or prickly pear," responded the computer. "The prickly pear plant is used to make the itchiest of all itching powders. Keep clear."

"Now we'll have to find a way around these plants," groaned Senna. "Or perhaps we should just go back to the ship and wait for them to approach us." And with that she turned around to head back, but what she saw made her let out a blood-curdling scream.

"Poison ivy!" she yelled. "Look out! There's a plant approaching and it looks like poison ivy! We're trapped!"

"Correct," the computer responded without waiting for the question from the captain.

"Set stunners to instant burn," Captain Carter calmly ordered.

The three crew members set their stunners to instant burn and aimed them at the poison ivy.

"Smoke from burning poison ivy will cause skin irritation," the computer commented, again not waiting for the question from the captain.

"Change stunners to five-minute freeze and... fire!" Captain Carter ordered as the poison ivy rapidly approached.

"Now we need a track through this prickly pear," she continued. "Change stunners to light laser and cut the track quickly. We have less than five minutes now before the freeze wears off the poison ivy."

We have less than five minutes now...

But it seemed that the prickly pear was somewhat immune to the laser beams and it took the three women longer than anticipated to cut the track. By the time they were through, the poison ivy was advancing menacingly again.

"Run!" commanded Captain Carter. So they ran. But as they did, harmless-looking trees stretched their branches out, seemingly trying to capture the crew.

Suddenly, Franny tripped and fell over a tree whose roots were snaking on top of the ground. As she frantically scrambled to her feet, its branches swooped down and encircled her, knocking her stunner out of her hands.

As Captain Carter and Senna stopped to help, some supplejack vines swung down from trees like playful monkeys and bound the women up, completely trapping them. There was no escape. Captain Carter, Senna, and Franny were then bundled up like packages and passed through the jungle from tree to tree until they reached the coast, where they were deposited unceremoniously in front of the giant redwood.

"You are trespassing here," boomed the resonant voice of the giant lindsay creek tree. "You have already disrupted our peaceful planet," it continued. "Now, tell me the purpose of your visit."

"We come in peace," replied Captain Carter. "We had not anticipated landing until your winter rye plant dragged us in. Our mission is to explore the fifth quadrant, looking for likely planets to settle. We were merely passing through your air space at the time."

"You must know that there are rules of passage when you wish to pass through air space," responded the tree. "You did not obey these rules so we had to assume that you were enemies. You were lucky we did not destroy your ship instantly when you did not respond to the silent signal."

"But we were caught by the winter rye plant and our systems went down before we received any silent signal," Franny answered. "Had we received a silent signal, we would have followed the rules of peaceful travel. We had no idea this planet was even inhabited."

"I will have to consult with the Council of Trees before deciding on your fate," the giant lindsay creek redwood tree said imperiously. "We may have to make examples of you so that others do not come to annoy us. Until then, you will be held captive."

While one group of trees moved off to a clearing to discuss the issue, the supplejack vines held the crew tightly.

"Computer – status? In silent mode please," Captain Carter whispered.

"The situation seems inescapable," replied the computer, not in its usual monotonous voice, but by a series of blinking lights that only the captain could understand. "But I have one suggestion. My database shows that the plants will be at their weakest during darkness and coldness. My suggestion is that you set your stunners to darkness and then to 30-minute freeze. That should weaken the plants enough to allow you to get back to the ship."

The captain whispered the computer's idea to the other two, and suddenly the area was as dark as a black hole.

"Thirty-minute freeze!" whispered Captain Carter, and within seconds, the supplejack began to fall away. Quickly the crew, directed by the computer, ran through the darkness back to the ship.

"Boost power systems as we approach and return them to the main console," Captain Carter said to the two crew members ahead of her, who used their wrist controllers to obey their captain's order.

"Alert! Alert!" the computer's voice broke into the blackness. "Poison ivy has become immune to the freeze. Prepare for attack from the rear!"

As the computer spoke, the leading poison ivy lunged ahead and brushed roughly up against Captain Carter, and, as Franny and Senna turned, they saw the poison ivy plant completely smother their captain.

"Reset stunners to stun then burn and... fire!" yelled Franny, assuming control. As she fired, Senna grabbed Captain Carter and dragged her away from the plant and through the hatchway into the safety of the ship.

"Prepare for emergency take-off," Franny said from the controls. "I can see that the heat from the instant burn is affecting the 30-minute freeze and soon the winter rye plant will have us in its clutches again."

And with that, the ship exploded into hyperdrive and hit a safe orbit from which they would try to return to base.

Safari POINT OF VIEW

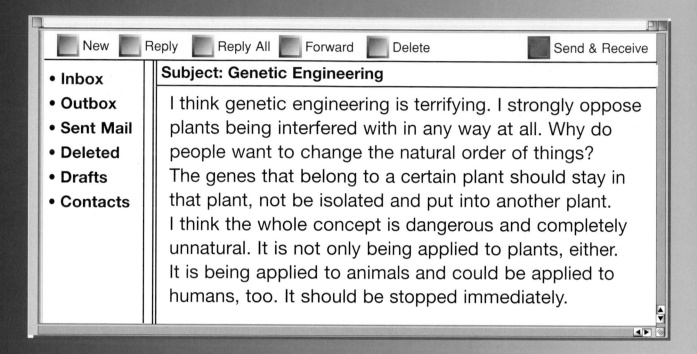

New | Reply | Reply All | Forward | Delete | Send & Receive

- **Inbox**
- **Outbox**
- **Sent Mail**
- **Deleted**
- **Drafts**
- **Contacts**

Subject: Genetic Engineering

I think genetic engineering is terrifying. I strongly oppose plants being interfered with in any way at all. Why do people want to change the natural order of things?
The genes that belong to a certain plant should stay in that plant, not be isolated and put into another plant.
I think the whole concept is dangerous and completely unnatural. It is not only being applied to plants, either. It is being applied to animals and could be applied to humans, too. It should be stopped immediately.

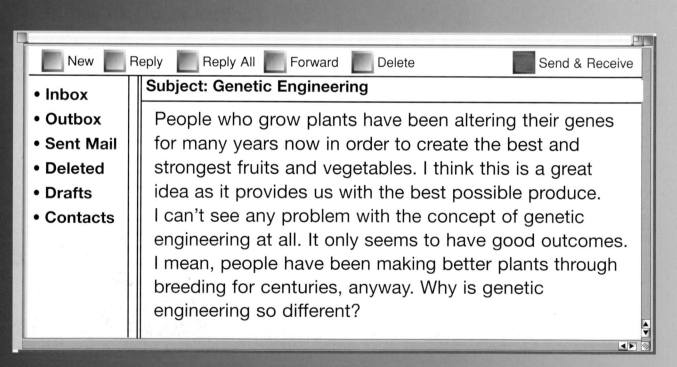

New | Reply | Reply All | Forward | Delete | Send & Receive

- **Inbox**
- **Outbox**
- **Sent Mail**
- **Deleted**
- **Drafts**
- **Contacts**

Subject: Genetic Engineering

People who grow plants have been altering their genes for many years now in order to create the best and strongest fruits and vegetables. I think this is a great idea as it provides us with the best possible produce.
I can't see any problem with the concept of genetic engineering at all. It only seems to have good outcomes.
I mean, people have been making better plants through breeding for centuries, anyway. Why is genetic engineering so different?

Safari POWER

anchorage
b – stable hold

minimal
a – least possible

evaporate
a – emit moisture

monotonous
c – unvarying

evasive
a – elusive

nutrients
c – nourishment

pores
b – tiny openings

excess
b – surplus

smother
a – cover and stifle

fragrance
c – sweet smell

menacingly
a – threateningly

tolerate
a – bear

a
b
c

Xtra for Xperts

What is a _host_?

Rating Scale

| 10-12 Excellent | 7-9 Very good | 4-6 Good | 0-3 Try again |

Trouble in the Forest

Written by Shilo Berry

Characters

| Grandma | Jody | Milly | Narrator | Tree 1 | Tree 2 |

Setting

The canopy layer of a forest

Scene 1

Tree 1
We have a problem in the forest. It appears an outsider is beginning to take over our forest and is strangling many of our trees.

Tree 2
I've seen the intruder you're talking about. It has thick roots that encircle the tree trunk like it's giving it a big hug. There's one over there.

Tree 1
Yes. Those big roots go right down to the floor of the forest. I guess that's how it manages to grow so fast. Look at that canopy of leaves it produces. It's blocking all the sunlight and moisture for the plants underneath it.

Tree 2
It grows halfway up a host tree, sending its roots around the tree and down to the ground. But the roots eventually strangle the host tree. From my position I can see into a garden. The original tree is in the garden.

Tree 1
But how did it travel into the forest?

Tree 2
I've been watching it. I think the birds eat the fruit. The fruit has seeds in the middle, but the birds cannot digest the seeds so they drop the seeds as they fly through the forest to the river.

Tree 1
Well, we need to do something to stop the plant from spreading or the whole forest will be in a lot of trouble.

Tree 2
How do you think we can stop the birds from flying through?

Tree 1

I don't think that would be the best solution. I think we need to go to the root of the problem, if you know what I mean. We need to get rid of that first tree and all the others that have grown from it.

Tree 2

I know the garden where the first plant is located. It is owned by a woman who has a granddaughter called Milly who is always playing in the garden. Perhaps we can get a message to her somehow.

Tree 1

A message? How on earth are trees supposed to get messages to humans! It's not possible!

Tree 2

Let's think about what we have that could help us do that.

Tree 1

What about our leaves? We could spell out a message somehow using them.

Tree 2

That's a good idea. I could drop some leaves over the fence to make a message on the ground in the garden.

Tree 1

It's not the right time of the year for dropping our leaves.

Tree 2

Then that should make it even more noticeable.

Tree 1

How would we get Milly to notice the message?

Tree 2

She plays outside every day after school. I can reach some of my branches right over by where she plays. I can drop the leaves to make a message there.

Tree 1

Sounds good. What are we going to write in the message?

Tree 2

What about *Help! There is a dangerous tree in the forest*?

Tree 1
That sounds good to me. We'll give it a try tomorrow.

Scene 2

Narrator
Tree 2 is reaching its branches over the fence into the garden. Milly and her friend Jody come running out into the garden.

Tree 2
Wind, I wish you would stop blowing for a bit so I could
get these leaves to fall in the
right place.

Jody
Gosh, you're so lucky to have such a lovely garden.

Milly
Yeah, I know. I love it. What I love the best are those big trees that lean over the fence and make shady places to sit. Hey, that's funny, look at that tree! It's dropping a lot of its leaves.

Jody
What's funny about that?

Milly
It's the wrong time of year for trees to drop leaves. I hope the tree is all right; maybe it is dropping its leaves because it is not well.

Jody
Maybe the wind is just making them fall off.

Milly
You're probably right. Let's go and do our homework.

Scene 3

Narrator
The girls run back inside, leaving Tree 2 looking sad.

Tree 1
Sorry, folks, that plan didn't work. The wind was blowing the leaves all over the place so the message was unreadable. Milly and her friend saw the leaves falling but thought it was just because of the wind.

Tree 2
I guess we need another plan.

Tree 1
What other parts could we use to make a message?

Tree 2
What about your roots? Do you think you could make a message with your roots?

Tree 1
That sounds like a good idea.

Tree 2
It is, but the ground is covered with grass. I don't think Milly would see the message.

Tree 1
That's no good, then.

Tree 2
Hold on, I have an idea. Milly has a big sandbox in the garden that she used to play in when she was younger. You could easily write a message in there. The sand is a bit wet at the moment so the message would be easy to see.

Tree 1
Great. Let's try it tomorrow.

Scene 4

Narrator
Tree 1 is stretching its roots over the sandbox and is writing the message in the sand. Milly arrives with her dog, Scamper.

Tree 1
That looks really good, if I do say so myself. It should be easy for Milly to read.

Milly
Scamper, Scamper, come here, boy. No, don't play in the sandbox or we'll have to give you a bath to get all the sand out of your coat.

Tree 1
Oh no! Where did that dog come from? Get out of there, dog! Get out! You're messing up my message.

Narrator
Milly grabs Scamper and throws a ball over to the other side of the garden for him to fetch. Tree 1 turns to the other trees.

Tree 1

Another plan down the tubes. I don't know where that dog came from but he messed up the message before Milly had time to read it.

Tree 2

Well, we just need to come up with another plan. What other suggestions are there?

Tree 1

I don't have any.

Tree 2

Neither do I. Hold on a second. The first plan was ruined by the wind. Perhaps we could get the wind to help us in some way.

Tree 1

We could tunnel the wind through our branches and leaves so it speaks our message as it rustles through them.

Tree 2

I know what you're saying. Listen to what happens when I hold my branches this way.

Narrator

The wind whistles through the branches making the tree sound like it's saying, 'Help!'

Tree 2

Hey, that's good. What if I hold my leaves this way?

Narrator

The wind rustles through the leaves, making it sound like the tree is saying, 'Dangerous tree.'

Tree 1

My turn again. What about if I hold my leaves and branches this way?

Narrator

Now the tree sounds like it's saying, 'In the forest.'

Tree 1

My turn. What if I lean over and hold my leaves this way?

Narrator

The wind rustles through the leaves, making it sound like the tree is saying, 'Milly.'

Tree 1

Looks like we're all set to try it out after school tomorrow.

Scene 5

Narrator
The next afternoon, Milly, Jody, and her grandma are sitting in the garden having an afternoon snack.

Tree 1
OK. Milly's in the garden with her grandma and Jody.

Tree 2
I'll start.

Narrator
The wind rustles through the leaves, making it sound like the tree is saying 'Milly, Milly, Milly.'

Milly
Can you hear that, Grandma? It sounds to me like the wind is calling my name.

Grandma
It did sound a bit like your name. But I don't think it was.

Tree 1
I'll try again.

Narrator
The wind starts calling Milly's name again, 'Milly, Milly, Milly.'

Milly
It is calling my name. How funny.

Tree 1
My turn.

Narrator
The wind starts saying, 'Help!'

Milly
It sounded like the wind was asking for my help.

Jody
Sometimes when the wind whistles through trees it sounds like it's calling to people.

Tree 2
Now me again.

Narrator
Now the wind is saying, 'Dangerous tree in the forest.'

Milly
Did you hear that, Grandma? I'm pretty sure it said that a dangerous tree is in the forest.

Grandma
I'm sure it's just the wind rustling through the trees. I think I'll go and get the dinner on now.

Scene 6

Narrator
Milly's grandma goes off, leaving her and Jody in the garden.

Milly
Shall we take Scamper for a walk in the forest?

Jody
I'd like that. Let's go.

Narrator
They go through the gate into the forest. It doesn't take long for Milly to notice the problem.

Milly
Look at that, Jody. That tree is being killed by that other type of tree that is hugging it with those large gripping roots and over there is another one. I wonder if this is what the wind was trying to tell me.

Jody
My goodness, Milly, you're right! It is strangling those poor trees.

Milly
Quick! We must go and tell Grandma what we've found.

Narrator
Milly, Jody, and Scamper run back to the house.

Milly
Grandma, I think the trees were trying to use the wind to get a message to us. There is a dangerous tree in the forest. It's killing the trees by hugging them with great big roots. We found that it's spreading. We really need to do something about it.

Grandma
That doesn't sound good. I would hate for those beautiful big trees to be in danger. Perhaps we should telephone the Park and Forest Protection Society. I'm sure they would be able to help us.

Milly
Thanks, Grandma.

Tree 1 and 2 (together)
Thanks, Milly!

The Secret Lives of Plants

Written by Michele Paul • Illustrated by Paul Konye

There once was a little sunflower,
Who wanted to have lots of power.
She grew and she grew,
Till she dwarfed quite a few,
That powerful big sunflower.

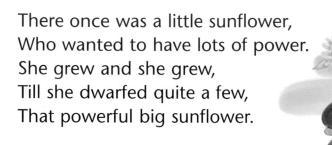

There once was a large oak tree,
Who was lonely as can be.
He wanted to be small,
But he was oh, so tall,
That large and lonely oak tree.

There once was a wandering weed,
Who liked to feed and to feed.
She grew and she grew,
Till the garden she spread through,
That enormous wandering weed.

There once was a tropical palm,
Who strangely grew on a farm.
I must cut you right down,
The farmer said with a frown,
To the beautiful tropical palm.

There once was a giant bean stalk,
Who desperately wanted to walk.
He tried and he tried,
Then he sat down and cried,
That poor old giant bean stalk.

readingsafari.com

Check out these Safari magazines, too!

Have your say -

e-mail your Safari Tour Guide at
tourguide@readingsafari.com

| New | Reply | Reply All | Forward | Delete | | Send & Receive |

- Inbox
- Outbox
- Sent Mail
- Deleted
- Drafts

Subject: Plant World

Now you have read this magazine, is there anything you feel strongly about? E-mail your point of view to the Safari Tour Guide.

Find some fun things to do!

Go to –
http://www.readingsafari.com

Safari Superstar

Name – Jody Hudston

Find out more about this Safari Superstar at

http://www.readingsafari.com